Introduction to costing

Workbook

Aubrey Penning

AAT WISE GUIDES – for convenient exam revision

This handy pocket-sized guide provides the **perfect study and revision resource** for the AAT Level 2 Certificate in Accounting.

available for:
  Bookkeeping 1
  Bookkeeping 2
  Working in Accounting and Finance
  Introduction to Costing

Visit www.osbornebooks.co.uk for further information and to place your order.

Published by Osborne Books Limited
Unit 1B Everoak Estate
Bromyard Road, Worcester WR2 5HP
Tel 01905 748071
Email books@osbornebooks.co.uk
Website www.osbornebooks.co.uk

Design by Laura Ingham

Printed by CPI Group (UK) Limited, Croydon, CR0 4YY, on environmentally friendly, acid-free paper from managed forests.

MIX
Paper from responsible sources
FSC® C013604

British Library Cataloguing in Publication Data
A catalogue record for this book is available from the British Library

ISBN 978 1909173 118

Contents

Introduction

Chapter activities

Chapter activities – answers

Practice assessments – tasks

Practice assessments – answers

Acknowledgements

The publisher wishes to thank the following for their help with the reading and production of the book: Jon Moore and Cathy Turner. Thanks are also due to Lynn Watkins for her technical editorial work and to Laura Ingham for her designs for this series.

The publisher is indebted to the Association of Accounting Technicians for its help and advice to our author and editors during the preparation of this text.

Author

Aubrey Penning has many years experience of teaching accountancy on a variety of courses in Worcester and Gwent. He is a Certified Accountant, and before his move into full-time teaching he worked for the health service, a housing association and a chemical supplier. Until recently he was the AAT course coordinator at Worcester College of Technology, specialising in the areas of management accounting and taxation.

Introduction

what this book covers

This book has been written to cover the Unit 'Basic costing' which is mandatory for the revised (2013) AAT Level 2 Certificate in Accounting.

what this book contains

This book is set out in two sections:

- **Chapter Activities** which provide extra practice material in addition to the activities included in the Osborne Books Tutorial text. Answers to the Chapter activities are set out in this book.

- **Practice Assessments** are included to prepare the student for the Computer Based Assessments. They are based directly on the structure, style and content of the sample assessment material provided by the AAT at www.aat.org.uk. Suggested answers to the Practice assessments are set out in this book.

further information

If you want to know more about our products, please visit www.osbornebooks.co.uk for further details and access to our online shop.

Chapter activities

1   The costing system

1.1   The table below lists some of the characteristics of financial accounting and management accounting systems. Indicate two characteristics for each system by putting a tick in the relevant column of the table below.

✔

Characteristic	Financial Accounting	Management Accounting
Records transactions that have already happened		
Provides accounts that comply with legal requirements		
Looks in detail at future costs and income of products and services		
May use estimates where these are the most suitable form of information		

1.2   Hideaway Ltd is a manufacturer of garden sheds.

Classify the following costs into materials, labour or overheads by putting a tick in the relevant column of the table below.

✔

Cost	Materials	Labour	Overheads
Wood used to make sheds			
Insurance of factory			
Wages of employees who cut window glass to size			
Wages of carpenter who assembles shed panels			

1.3   Hideaway Ltd is a manufacturer of garden sheds.

Classify the following costs by nature (direct or indirect) by putting a tick in the relevant column of the table below.

Cost	Direct	Indirect
Wood used to make sheds		
Insurance of factory		
Wages of employees who cut window glass to size		
Wages of carpenter who assembles shed panels		

1.4   Dave's Plaice is a take away fish and chip shop.

Classify the following costs by putting a tick in the relevant column of the table below.

Cost	Direct Materials	Direct Labour	Indirect Costs
Potatoes used to make chips			
Maintenance of cooking equipment			
Wages of employees who fry fish and chips			
Gas to cook fish and chips			

1.5   Trendy Limited manufactures clothing.

Classify the following costs by function (production, administration, or selling and distribution) by putting a tick in the relevant column of the table below.

✔

Cost	Production	Administration	Selling and Distribution
Purchases of cloth			
Salespeople's salaries			
Insurance of office building			
Salaries of sewing machinists			

2 Cost centres and cost behaviour

2.1 Falcon Ltd is a manufacturer of toys.

Classify the following costs by their behaviour (fixed, variable, or semi-variable) by putting a tick in the relevant column of the table below.

✔

Cost	Fixed	Variable	Semi-Variable
Managers' salaries			
Production workers paid a fixed wage plus a production-based bonus			
Packaging materials for finished toys			
Factory insurance			

2.2 Omega Ltd, a manufacturer of furniture, uses a numerical coding structure based on one profit centre and three cost centres as outlined below. Each code has a sub-code so each transaction will be coded as ***/***

Profit/Cost Centre	Code	Sub-classification	Sub-code
Sales	100	UK Sales	100
		Overseas Sales	200
Production	200	Direct Cost	100
		Indirect Cost	200
Administration	300	Indirect Cost	200
Selling and Distribution	400	Indirect Cost	200

Code the following income and expense transactions, which have been extracted from purchase invoices, sales invoices and payroll, using the table below.

Transaction	Code
Factory lighting	
Warehouse repairs	
Sales to Newcastle, UK	
Sales to India	
Materials to upholster chairs	
Factory maintenance wages	

2.3   Smooth Running Limited operates a garage that repairs and maintains cars. It uses a coding system for its costs (materials, labour or overheads) and then further classifies each cost by nature (direct or indirect cost) as below. So, for example, the code for direct materials is A100.

Element of Cost	Code	Nature of Cost	Code
Materials	A	Direct	100
		Indirect	200
Labour	B	Direct	100
		Indirect	200
Overheads	C	Direct	100
		Indirect	200

Code the following costs, extracted from invoices and payroll, using the table below.

Cost	Code
Wages of trainee mechanic	
Wages of receptionist	B200
Oil used for car servicing	
Depreciation of electronic tuning equipment used for car servicing	
Replacement parts used for car repairs	

2.4 Complete the table below showing fixed costs, variable costs, total costs and unit cost at the different levels of production. Calculate unit cost to the nearest penny where appropriate.

Units	Fixed Costs	Variable Costs	Total Costs	Unit Cost
1,000	£20,000	£5,000	£25,000	£25.00
2,000	£	£	£	£
3,000	£	£	£	£
4,000	£	£	£	£

2.5 Omega Ltd is costing a single product which has the following cost details:

Variable Costs per unit

Materials	£5
Labour	£4
Total Fixed Overheads	£90,000

Complete the following total cost and unit cost table for a production level of 15,000 units.

	Total Cost	Unit Cost
Materials	£	£
Labour	£	£
Fixed Overheads	£	£
Total	£	£

2.6 Highstyle Limited is a company that owns two hairdressing salons. One salon is called Bonkers, and the other is called Hats-off. Each salon is an investment centre.

The following is an extract from the coding manual used by the company.

Investment Centre	Code
Bonkers Salon	B
Hats-off Salon	H
Revenue, Cost, or Investment	**Code**
Salon sales revenue	100
Salon purchase of hair products	200
Labour costs	300
Overheads	400
Investment in shop assets	900

Each code consists of a letter followed by a 3 digit number.

Complete the following table with the appropriate codes.

Transaction	Code
Sales in Bonkers Salon	
Purchase of new barber chair for Hats-off Salon	
Purchase of new wall mirrors for Bonkers Salon	
Purchase of hair products for Bonkers Salon	
Cost of rent at Bonkers shop	
Cost of paying wages of Hats-off stylist	

3 Inventory valuation and the manufacturing account

3.1 Identify the correct inventory (stock) valuation method from the characteristic given by putting a tick in the relevant column of the table below.

Characteristic	FIFO	LIFO	AVCO
Issues of inventory are valued at the oldest purchase cost			
Issues of inventory are valued at the average of the cost of purchases			
Inventory balance is valued at the most recent purchase cost			

3.2 Identify whether the following statements about inventory (stock) valuation are true or false by putting a tick in the relevant column of the table below.

	True	False
FIFO costs issues of inventory at the average purchase price		
AVCO costs issues of inventory at the oldest purchase price		
LIFO costs issues of inventory at the most recent purchase price		
LIFO values inventory balance at the most recent purchase price		
FIFO values inventory balance at the most recent purchase price		
AVCO values inventory balance at the latest purchase price		

3.3 Omega Ltd has the following movements in a certain type of inventory into and out of its stores for the month of March:

Date	Receipts		Issues	
	Units	Cost	Units	Cost
March 5	300	£900		£
March 8	200	£800		£
March 12	500	£2,200		£
March 18			600	£
March 25	400	£2,000		£

Complete the table below for the issue and closing inventory values.

Method	Value of Issue on 18 March	Inventory at 31 March
FIFO	£	£
LIFO	£	£
AVCO	£	£

3.4 Place the following headings and amounts into the correct format of a manufacturing account on the right side of the table, making sure that the arithmetic of your account is accurate. The first entry has been made for you.

	£		£
Direct cost		Opening inventory of raw materials	10,000
Opening inventory of raw materials	10,000		
Closing inventory of work in progress	19,000		
Direct labour	30,000		
Opening inventory of work in progress	10,000		
Closing inventory of finished goods	14,000		
Closing inventory of raw materials	11,000		
Cost of goods sold			
Raw materials used in manufacture	43,000		
Purchases of raw materials	44,000		
Cost of goods manufactured			
Opening inventory of finished goods	25,000		
Manufacturing overheads	21,000		
Manufacturing cost			

Calculate the following amounts:
- Direct cost
- Manufacturing cost
- Cost of goods manufactured
- Cost of goods sold

3.5 Magnum Ltd has the following movements in a certain type of inventory into and out of its stores for the month of September:

Date	Receipts		Issues	
	Units	**Cost**	**Units**	**Cost**
September 5	400	£800		£
September 8	250	£450		£
September 12			300	£
September 18	500	£1,200		£
September 25	400	£1,000		£

Complete the table below for the issue and closing inventory values.

Calculate final values to nearest £.

Method	Value of Issue on September 12	Inventory at 30 September
FIFO	£	£
LIFO	£	£
AVCO	£	£

4 Labour costs

4.1 Identify the labour payment method by putting a tick in the relevant column of the table below.

✔

Payment Method	Time-rate	Piecework	Time-rate plus bonus
Labour is paid based entirely on the production level achieved			
Labour is paid according to hours worked, plus an extra amount if an agreed level of output is exceeded			
Labour is paid only according to hours worked			

4.2 Greville Ltd pays a time-rate of £12 per hour to its direct labour for a standard 38 hour week. Any of the labour force working in excess of 38 hours is paid an overtime rate of £18 per hour.

Calculate the gross wage for the week for the two workers in the table below.

Worker	Hours Worked	Basic Wage	Overtime	Gross Wage
A Summer	38	£	£	£
S Cambridge	43	£	£	£

4.3 Omega Ltd uses a piecework method to pay labour in one of its factories. The rate used is £1.30 per unit produced.

Calculate the gross wage for the week for the two workers in the table below.

Worker	Units Produced in Week	Gross Wage
V Singh	320	£
A Evans	390	£

4.4 Omega uses a time-rate method with bonus to pay its direct labour in one of its factories. The time-rate used is £10 per hour and a worker is expected to produce 20 units an hour. Anything over this and the worker is paid a bonus of £0.25 per unit.

Calculate the gross wage for the week including bonus for the three workers in the table below.

Worker	Hours Worked	Units Produced	Basic Wage	Bonus	Gross Wage
A Samuel	35	650	£	£	£
J McGovern	35	775	£	£	£
M Schaeffer	35	705	£	£	£

4.5 Identify the following statements as true or false by putting a tick in the relevant column of the table below.

✔

	True	False
Indirect labour costs can be identified with the goods being made or the service being produced		
Direct labour costs never alter when the level of activity changes		
The classification of labour costs into direct and indirect does not depend on the method of calculation of the pay		

5 Providing information and using spreadsheets

5.1 Identify the following statements as being true or false by putting a tick in the relevant column of the table below.

✔

	True	False
A budget is a financial plan for an organisation that is prepared in advance		
If actual costs are more than budgeted costs the result is a favourable variance		

5.2 Greville Ltd has produced a performance report detailing budgeted and actual cost for last month.

Calculate the amount of the variance for each cost type and then determine whether it is adverse or favourable by putting a tick in the relevant column of the table below.

Cost Type	Budget £	Actual £	Variance	Adverse	Favourable
Direct Materials	93,500	94,200	£		
Direct Labour	48,700	47,800	£		
Production Overheads	28,000	31,200	£		
Administration Overheads	28,900	27,700	£		
Selling and Distribution Overheads	23,800	23,100	£		

5.3   The following performance report for last month has been produced for Greville Ltd as summarised in the table below. Any variance in excess of 4% of budget is thought to be significant and should be reported to the relevant manager for review and appropriate action.

Examine the variances in the table below and indicate whether they are significant or not significant by putting a tick in the relevant column.

✔

Cost Type	Budget £	Variance	Adverse/ Favourable	Significant	Not Significant
Direct Materials	93,500	£700	A		
Direct Labour	48,700	£900	F		
Production Overheads	28,000	£3,200	A		
Administration Overheads	28,900	£1,200	F		
Selling and Distribution Overheads	23,800	£700	F		

5.4 Monitor Limited uses a spreadsheet to present budgeted and actual data and calculate profit and variances. The following spreadsheet has been partly completed.

	A	B	C	D	E
1		Budget £	Actual £	Variance £	A / F
2	Income	450,000	446,000		
3	Materials	114,500	114,600		
4	Labour	123,100	119,000		
5	Overheads	170,500	174,100		
6	Profit				

Required:

- Enter A or F into each cell in column E to denote adverse or favourable variances.

- Enter appropriate formulas into the cells in column D to calculate variances, and into the remaining cells in row 6 to calculate profit.

5.5 Locale Ltd makes a single product and for a production level of 18,000 units has the following cost details:

Direct Materials   6,000 kilos   at £27 per kilo

Direct Labour   9,000 hours   at £10 an hour

Overheads   £36,000

(a) Complete the table below to show the unit cost at the production level of 18,000 units.

	A	B
1	**Element**	**Unit Cost**
2	Materials	£
3	Labour	£
4	Overheads	£
5	Total	£

(b) Show formulas that could have been used to calculate the figures in cells B2, B3, B4 and B5.

Chapter
activities
answers

1   The costing system

1.1

Characteristic	Financial Accounting	Management Accounting
Records transactions that have already happened	✔	
Provides accounts that comply with legal requirements	✔	
Looks in detail at future costs and income of products and services		✔
May use estimates where these are the most suitable form of information		✔

1.2

Cost	Materials	Labour	Overheads
Wood used to make sheds	✔		
Insurance of factory			✔
Wages of employees who cut window glass to size		✔	
Wages of carpenter who assembles shed panels		✔	

1.3

Cost	Direct	Indirect
Wood used to make sheds	✔	
Insurance of factory		✔
Wages of employees who cut window glass to size	✔	
Wages of carpenter who assembles shed panels	✔	

1.4

Cost	Direct Materials	Direct Labour	Indirect Costs
Potatoes used to make chips	✔		
Maintenance of cooking equipment			✔
Wages of employees who fry fish and chips		✔	
Gas to cook fish and chips			✔

1.5

Cost	Production	Administration	Selling and Distribution
Purchases of cloth	✔		
Salespeople's salaries			✔
Insurance of office building		✔	
Salaries of sewing machinists	✔		

2 Cost centres and cost behaviour

2.1

Cost	Fixed	Variable	Semi-Variable
Managers' salaries	✔		
Production workers paid a fixed wage plus a production-based bonus			✔
Packaging materials for finished toys		✔	
Factory insurance	✔		

2.2

Transaction	Code
Factory lighting	200/200
Warehouse repairs	400/200
Sales to Newcastle, UK	100/100
Sales to India	100/200
Materials to upholster chairs	200/100
Factory maintenance wages	200/200

2.3

Cost	Code
Wages of trainee mechanic	B100
Wages of receptionist	B200
Oil used for car servicing	A100
Depreciation of electronic tuning equipment used for car servicing	C200
Replacement parts used for car repairs	A100

2.4

Units	Fixed Costs	Variable Costs	Total Costs	Unit Cost
1,000	£20,000	£5,000	£25,000	£25.00
2,000	£20,000	£10,000	£30,000	£15.00
3,000	£20,000	£15,000	£35,000	£11.67
4,000	£20,000	£20,000	£40,000	£10.00

2.5

	Total Cost	Unit Cost
Materials	£75,000	£5.00
Labour	£60,000	£4.00
Fixed Overheads	£90,000	£6.00
Total	£225,000	£15.00

2.6

Transaction	Code
Sales in Bonkers Salon	B100
Purchase of new barber chair for Hats-off Salon	H900
Purchase of new wall mirrors for Bonkers Salon	B900
Purchase of hair products for Bonkers Salon	B200
Cost of rent at Bonkers shop	B400
Cost of paying wages of Hats-off stylist	H300

3

Inventory valuation and the manufacturing account

3.1

Characteristic	FIFO	LIFO	AVCO
Issues of inventory are valued at the oldest purchase cost	✔		
Issues of inventory are valued at the average of the cost of purchases			✔
Inventory balance is valued at the most recent purchase cost	✔		

3.2

	True	False
FIFO costs issues of inventory at the average purchase price		✔
AVCO costs issues of inventory at the oldest purchase price		✔
LIFO costs issues of inventory at the most recent purchase price	✔	
LIFO values inventory balance at the most recent purchase price		✔
FIFO values inventory balance at the most recent purchase price	✔	
AVCO values inventory balance at the latest purchase price		✔

3.3

Method	Value of Issue on 18 March	Inventory at 31 March
FIFO	£2,140	£3,760
LIFO	£2,600	£3,300
AVCO	£2,340	£3,560

3.4

	£		£
Direct cost		Opening inventory of raw materials	10,000
Opening inventory of raw materials	10,000	Purchases of raw materials	44,000
Closing inventory of work in progress	19,000	Closing inventory of raw materials	11,000
Direct labour	30,000	Raw materials used in manufacture	43,000
Opening inventory of work in progress	10,000	Direct labour	30,000
Closing inventory of finished goods	14,000	Direct cost	
Closing inventory of raw materials	11,000	Manufacturing overheads	21,000
Cost of goods sold		Manufacturing cost	
Raw materials used in manufacture	43,000	Opening inventory of work in progress	10,000
Purchases of raw materials	44,000	Closing inventory of work in progress	19,000
Cost of goods manufactured		Cost of goods manufactured	
Opening inventory of finished goods	25,000	Opening inventory of finished goods	25,000
Manufacturing overheads	21,000	Closing inventory of finished goods	14,000
Manufacturing cost		Cost of goods sold	

- Direct cost £73,000
- Manufacturing cost £94,000
- Cost of goods manufactured £85,000
- Cost of goods sold £96,000

3.5

Method	Value of Issue on September 12	Inventory at 30 September
FIFO	£600	£2,850
LIFO	£550	£2,900
AVCO	£577	£2,873

4 Labour costs

4.1

Payment Method	Time-rate	Piecework	Time-rate plus bonus
Labour is paid based entirely on the production level achieved		✔	
Labour is paid according to hours worked, plus an extra amount if an agreed level of output is exceeded			✔
Labour is paid only according to hours worked	✔		

4.2

Worker	Hours Worked	Basic Wage	Overtime	Gross Wage
A Summer	38	£456	£0	£456
S Cambridge	43	£456	£90	£546

4.3

Worker	Units Produced in Week	Gross Wage
V Singh	320	£416.00
A Evans	390	£507.00

4.4

Worker	Hours Worked	Units Produced	Basic Wage	Bonus	Gross Wage
A Samuel	35	650	£350.00	£0.00	£350.00
J McGovern	35	775	£350.00	£18.75	£368.75
M Schaeffer	35	705	£350.00	£1.25	£351.25

4.5

	True	False
Indirect labour costs can be identified with the goods being made or the service being produced		✔
Direct labour costs never alter when the level of activity changes		✔
The classification of labour costs into direct and indirect does not depend on the method of calculation of the pay	✔	

5   Providing information and using spreadsheets

5.1

	True	False
A budget is a financial plan for an organisation that is prepared in advance	✔	
If actual costs are more than budgeted costs the result is a favourable variance		✔

5.2

Cost Type	Budget £	Actual £	Variance	Adverse	Favourable
Direct Materials	93,500	94,200	£700	✔	
Direct Labour	48,700	47,800	£900		✔
Production Overheads	28,000	31,200	£3,200	✔	
Administration Overheads	28,900	27,700	£1,200		✔
Selling and Distribution Overheads	23,800	23,100	£700		✔

5.3

Cost Type	Budget £	Variance	Adverse/ Favourable	Significant	Not Significant
Direct Materials	93,500	£700	A		✔
Direct Labour	48,700	£900	F		✔
Production Overheads	28,000	£3,200	A	✔	
Administration Overheads	28,900	£1,200	F	✔	
Selling and Distribution Overheads	23,800	£700	F		✔

5.4

	A	B	C	D	E
1		Budget £	Actual £	Variance £	A / F
2	Income	450,000	446,000	=B2-C2	A
3	Materials	114,500	114,600	=C3-B3	A
4	Labour	123,100	119,000	=B4-C4	F
5	Overheads	170,500	174,100	=C5-B5	A
6	Profit	=B2-B3-B4-B5	=C2-C3-C4-C5	=B6-C6	A

Other valid formulas could be used.

5.5   (a)

	A	B
1	**Element**	**Unit Cost**
2	Materials	£9.00
3	Labour	£5.00
4	Overheads	£2.00
5	Total	£16.00

(b)   Cell B2:   =(6000*27)/18000

Cell B3:   =(9000*10)/18000

Cell B4:   =36000/18000

Cell B5:   =B2+B3+B4

Other valid formulas could be used.

Practice
assessment 1

Task 1(a)

Identify the following statements as true or false by putting a tick in the relevant column of the table below.

Statement	True	False
LIFO is a method of paying labour		
Standard costs may be used to help build budgets		
Variances can measure the difference between budgeted and actual income and costs		
Fixed costs will never change in the future whatever happens		

(b)

The table below lists some of the characteristics of financial accounting and management accounting systems.

Indicate which characteristics relate to each system by putting a tick in the relevant column of the table below.

Characteristic	Financial Accounting	Management Accounting
It is concerned with recording historic costs and revenues		
One of its main purposes is to provide information for annual financial statements		
It is accurate, with no use of estimates		
It looks forward to show what is likely to happen in the future		

Task 2(a)

Octavia Ltd is a manufacturer of food products.

Classify the following costs into materials, labour or expenses by putting a tick in the relevant column of the table below.

Cost	Materials	Labour	Overheads
Meat used in burgers			
Electricity used in factory			
Boxes to pack burgers			
Expenses of the sales manager			

(b)

Citicars Ltd is in business as a taxi company.

Classify the following costs by nature (direct or indirect) by putting a tick in the relevant column of the table below.

✔

Cost	Direct	Indirect
Fuel for taxis		
Cost of servicing taxis		
Wages of taxi drivers		
Wages of reception staff		

Task 3(a)

Granville Ltd manufactures mobile telephones from components.

Classify the following costs by function (production, administration, or selling and distribution) by putting a tick in the relevant column of the table below.

✔

Cost	Production	Administration	Selling and Distribution
Purchases of components for mobile telephones			
Commission paid to sales staff			
Rent of offices			
Wages of staff who assemble telephones			

(b)

Fanfare Ltd is a manufacturer of musical instruments.

Classify the following costs by their behaviour (fixed, variable, or semi-variable) by putting a tick in the relevant column of the table below.

Cost	Fixed	Variable	Semi-Variable
Labour costs paid on a time basis			
Maintenance of website			
Power costs which include a standing charge			
Packing materials for completed instruments			

Task 4

Citicars Limited operates a taxi business and uses a coding system for its costs of materials, labour or overheads, and then further classifies each cost by nature (direct or indirect cost) as below. So, for example, the code for direct materials is 50/100.

Cost	Code	Nature of Cost	Code
Materials	50	Direct	100
		Indirect	200
Labour	60	Direct	100
		Indirect	200
Overheads	70	Direct	100
		Indirect	200

Code the following costs, extracted from invoices and payroll, using the table below.

Cost	Code
Wages of taxi driver	
Vehicle insurance for taxis	
Wages of reception staff	
Fuel for taxis	
Office rent	

Task 5

Octavia Ltd, a manufacturer of food products, uses an alpha-numeric coding structure based on one profit centre and three cost centres as outlined below. Each code has a sub-code so each transaction will be coded as */***

Profit/Cost Centre	Code	Sub-classification	Sub-code
Sales	A	Restaurant Sales	100
		Supermarket Sales	200
Production	B	Direct Cost	100
		Indirect Cost	200
Administration	C	Direct Cost	100
		Indirect Cost	200
Selling and Distribution	D	Direct Cost	100
		Indirect Cost	200

Code the following revenue and expense transactions, which have been extracted from purchase invoices, sales invoices and payroll, using the table below.

Transaction	Code
Factory lighting	
Repairs to warehouse	
Meat for making burgers	
Sales to 'Kings Restaurant'	
Commission to sales staff	
Stationery for Administration	

Task 6(a)

Identify the following statements as either true or false by putting a tick in the relevant column of the table below.

✔

	True	False
Variable costs change in proportion to changes in activity level		
Fixed costs remain unchanged when activity levels change		
Semi-variable costs change in proportion to changes in activity level		

(b)

Classify the following costs as either fixed or variable by putting a tick in the relevant column of the table below.

✔

Cost	Fixed	Variable
Factory insurance		
Bonus for production staff paid per item produced		
Salaries of administration staff		
Repairs to a factory used for production		

Task 7(a)

Identify the following statements as true or false by putting a tick in the relevant column of the table below.

	True	False
Direct material costs cannot be identified with the goods being made or the service being produced		
Indirect costs never change when the level of activity alters		

(b)

Eureka Ltd makes a single product and for a production level of 15,000 units has the following cost details:

Direct Materials	7,500 kilos	at £6 per kilo
Direct Labour	3,750 hours	at £11 an hour
Overheads		£60,000

Complete the table below to show the unit cost at the production level of 15,000 units.

Element	Unit Cost
Materials	£
Labour	£
Overheads	£
Total	£

Task 8(a)

Reorder the following costs into a manufacturing account format on the right side of the table below.

	£		£
Closing inventory of raw materials	10,000		
Direct labour	86,000		
Opening inventory of raw materials	9,000		
Closing inventory of finished goods	25,000		
Direct cost			
Cost of goods manufactured			
Cost of sales			
Manufacturing cost			
Purchases of raw materials	48,000		
Opening inventory of work in progress	9,000		
Opening inventory of finished goods	30,000		
Manufacturing overheads	64,000		
Direct materials used			
Closing inventory of work in progress	11,000		

(b)

Enter the correct figures for the following costs related to part (a):

Direct materials used	£
Direct cost	£
Manufacturing cost	£
Cost of goods manufactured	£
Cost of sales	£

Task 9(a)

Identify the correct inventory (stock) valuation method from the characteristic given by putting a tick in the relevant column of the table below.

Characteristic	FIFO	LIFO	AVCO
Inventory is valued at the most recent purchase cost			
Issues are valued at the average of the cost of purchases			
Issues are valued at the oldest relevant purchase cost			

(b)

Identify whether the following statements are true or false by putting a tick in the relevant column of the table below.

	True	False
AVCO costs issues of inventory at the most recent purchase price		
FIFO costs issues of inventory at the oldest relevant purchase price		
LIFO costs issues of inventory at the oldest relevant purchase price		
FIFO values closing inventory at the most recent purchase price		
LIFO values closing inventory at the most recent purchase price		
AVCO values closing inventory at the most recent purchase price		

Task 10

Octavia Ltd has the following movements in a certain type of inventory (stock) into and out of its stores for the month of August:

Date	Receipts		Issues	
	Units	Cost	Units	Cost
August 12	100	£500		£
August 14	350	£1,820		£
August 17	400	£2,200		£
August 18			700	£
August 26	300	£1,680		£

Complete the table below for the issue and closing inventory values.

Method	Value of Issue on 18 August	Inventory at 31 August
FIFO	£	£
LIFO	£	£
AVCO	£	£

Task 11(a)

Identify the labour payment method by putting a tick in the relevant column of the table below.

✔

Payment Method	Time-rate	Piecework	Time-rate plus bonus
Labour is paid based entirely on attendance at the workplace			
Labour is paid a basic rate plus an extra amount if an agreed level of production is exceeded			
Labour is paid entirely according to each individual's output			

(b)

Granville Ltd pays a time-rate of £8 per hour to its direct labour for a standard 37 hour week. Any of the labour force working in excess of 37 hours is paid an overtime rate of £16 per hour.

Calculate the gross wage for the week for the two workers in the table below.

Worker	Hours Worked	Basic Wage	Overtime	Gross Wage
A Smith	37	£	£	£
S Collins	41	£	£	£

Task 12

Octavia Ltd uses a piecework method to pay labour in one of its factories. The rate used is £2.16 per unit produced.

Calculate the gross wage for the week for the two workers in the table below.

Worker	Units Produced in Week	Gross Wage
G Powell	109	£
S Singh	123	£

Task 13

Octavia Ltd uses a time-rate method with bonus to pay its direct labour in one of its factories. The time-rate used is £10 per hour and a worker is expected to produce 7 units an hour. Anything over this and the worker is paid a bonus of £0.50 per unit.

Calculate the gross wage for the week including bonus for the three workers in the table below.

Worker	Hours Worked	Units Produced	Basic Wage	Bonus	Gross Wage
A Weaton	40	250	£	£	£
J Davis	40	295	£	£	£
M Laston	40	280	£	£	£

Task 14

A company has produced the following partial cost and revenue information for a product in various months:

Sales revenue per unit: £20

Variable costs per unit:

    Materials   £7

    Labour   £3

A spreadsheet has been partly completed to record the total costs and revenue.

	A	B	C	D	E	F	G
1	Month	Variable Materials £	Variable Labour £	Fixed Costs £		Sales Revenue £	
2	January	70,000	30,000	40,000	140,000	200,000	60,000
3	February	140,000					
4	March		45,000	40,000			
5	Total						

Required:

- Insert appropriate column headings into cells E1 and G1
  (select from: Total Variable Costs £; Total Fixed Costs £; Total Costs £; Profit £).

- Insert appropriate figures into the remaining cells in rows 3 and 4.

- Insert appropriate formulas into the cells in row 5.

Task 15

Identify the following statements about spreadsheets as being true or false by putting a tick in the relevant column.

Statement	True	False
A cell is identified by its location number followed by location letter (eg 6C)		
Every cell in a spreadsheet must always contain a formula		
Formulas can be used to automatically total rows or columns		
A spreadsheet workbook is a collection of spreadsheet worksheets		

Task 16

A company uses a spreadsheet to present budgeted and actual data and calculate profit and variances. The following spreadsheet has been partly completed.

	A	B	C	D	E
1		Budget £	Actual £	Variance £	A / F
2	Income	290,000	296,000		
3	Materials	144,500	150,600		
4	Labour	51,100	49,000		
5	Overheads	72,500	76,300		
6	Profit				

Required:

- Enter A or F into each cell in column E to denote adverse or favourable variances.

- Enter appropriate formulas into the cells in column D to calculate variances, and into the remaining cells in row 6 to calculate profit.

Task 17

The following spreadsheet has been partly completed. Variances are considered significant if they exceed 4% of the budgeted amount.

(a) Complete the spreadsheet as follows:

Complete column D with the amounts of the variances.

Show whether adverse (A) or Favourable (F) in column E.

Use 'S' to denote a significant variance or 'NS' to show a variance that is not significant in column F.

	A	B	C	D	E	F
1		Budget £	Actual £	Variance £	A / F	S/NS
2	Income	173,500	176,000			
3	Materials	62,500	71,600			
4	Labour	31,100	38,000			
5	Overheads	60,500	59,300			

(b) If the spreadsheet was to be sorted to show the largest variance first, which of the following functions would need to be used in conjunction with column D?

- Average
- Ascending
- Descending
- Autosum

Practice assessment 2

Task 1(a)

Identify the following statements as being true or false by putting a tick in the relevant column of the table below.

✔

	True	False
AVCO is a method of valuing inventory issues and balances		
One method of labour payment is to pay a basic hourly rate for normal working hours, and an enhanced rate for overtime hours		
Variances can only be used to measure the difference between budgeted and actual costs (not income)		
A fixed cost per unit will always remain unchanged as output volumes change		

(b)

Indicate the characteristics of financial accounting and management accounting by putting a tick in the relevant column of the table below.

✔

Characteristic	Financial Accounting	Management Accounting
The system is subject to many external regulations		
The accounts must be produced in a format that is imposed on the organisation		
The system is governed primarily by its usefulness to its internal users		
The information produced can be in any format that the organisation wishes to use		

Task 2

Wheeler Ltd is a manufacturer of bicycles.

(a) Classify the following costs that the company incurred by putting a tick in the relevant column of the table below.

✔

Cost	Material	Labour	Overhead
Factory rent			
Steel for manufacturing wheel spokes			
Pay of staff who assemble wheels			
Factory lighting			

(b)   Classify the following costs that the company incurred by putting a tick in the relevant column of the table below.

✔

Cost	Direct	Indirect
Cost of paying factory supervisor		
Cost of paying factory cleaner		
Cost of repairs to factory electrical system		
Cost of factory insurance		

Task 3

Wheeler Ltd is a manufacturer of bicycles.

(a)   Classify by function the following costs that the company incurred by putting a tick in the relevant column of the table below.

✔

Cost	Production	Administration	Selling and Distribution	Finance
Cost of paying factory supervisor				
Cost of servicing of delivery vehicles				
Cost of advertisements				
Cost of arrangement fee for bank overdraft				

(b)   Classify by behaviour the following costs that the company incurred by putting a tick in the relevant column of the table below.

✔

Cost	Fixed	Variable	Semi-Variable
Cost of paying wheel assemblers on a piecework basis			
Cost of renting factory premises			
Cost of advertisements			
Cost of paying a production supervisor on a basic pay plus a production-based bonus			

Task 4

SandS Ltd manufactures and sells beachwear. It uses a numerical coding structure based on one profit centre and three cost centres as outlined below. Each code has a sub-code, so each transaction will have a code format ***/***

Profit/Cost Centre	Code	Sub-classification	Sub-code
Sales	500	Men's wear	085
		Women's wear	095
Production	600	Direct cost	010
		Indirect cost	020
Administration	700	Direct cost	030
		Indirect cost	040
Selling and Distribution	800	Direct cost	050
		Indirect cost	060

Code the following transactions by entering the appropriate code in the table.

Transaction	Code
Wages of administration assistant	
Cost of producing sales catalogue	
Sales of men's swimming trunks	
Purchase of material to make clothing	
Wages of production supervisor	
Cost of renting photocopier for administration department	

Task 5

Spread Ltd manages projects in the UK and abroad. It uses an alpha numerical coding structure as outlined below. Each code has a sub-code, so each transaction will have a code format AB123.

Activity	Code	Sub-classification	Sub-code
Investment in projects	IP	UK projects	100
		Overseas projects	200
Project revenues	PR	UK projects	100
		Overseas projects	200
Project costs	PC	Material	030
		Labour	040
		Overheads	050

Code the following transactions by entering the appropriate code in the table.

Transaction	Code
Revenue from project in Saudi Arabia	
Cost of material used for project in Saudi Arabia	
Cost of hiring local labour for project in Saudi Arabia	
Investment in project in Saudi Arabia	
Revenue from UK project	
Cost of renting project offices	

Task 6(a)

Identify the cost behaviour described in each of the following statements by putting a tick in the relevant column of the table below.

Statement	Fixed	Variable	Semi-Variable
Costs are £4,000 in total for 1,000 units, and £6,000 in total for 1,500 units			
Costs of £20,000 in total for 2,000 units are made up of £10,000 plus £5 per unit			
Costs are £5 per unit at 20,000 units and £10 per unit at 10,000 units			

(b)

Classify the following costs by putting a tick in the relevant column of the table below.

Cost	Fixed	Variable
Cost of factory insurance		
Cost of interest on a bank loan		
Cost of raw materials used to manufacture products		

Task 7(a)

Indicate whether each of the following costs is a direct cost or not by putting a tick in the relevant column of the table below.

✔

Cost	Yes	No
Cost of factory insurance		
Cost of interest on a bank loan		
Cost of raw materials used to manufacture products		

(b)

A company makes a single product. At a production level of 50,000 units the following costs are incurred:

Direct Materials	25,000 kilos	at £4.00 per kilo
Direct Labour	5,000 hours	at £10.00 per hour
Overheads	£250,000	

Complete the following table to show the unit product cost at the production level of 50,000 units.

Element	Unit Product Cost
Direct materials	£
Direct labour	£
Direct cost	£
Overheads	£
Total cost	£

Task 8(a)

Reorder the following costs and descriptions into a manufacturing account format on the right side of the table below.

	£		£
Direct cost			
Purchases of raw materials	123,000		
Opening inventory of raw materials	13,000		
Closing inventory of finished goods	33,000		
Direct labour	156,000		
Cost of goods manufactured			
Cost of goods sold			
Manufacturing cost			
Direct materials used			
Opening inventory of work in progress	27,000		
Opening inventory of finished goods	35,000		
Manufacturing overheads	146,000		
Closing inventory of work in progress	39,000		
Closing inventory of raw materials	27,000		

(b)

Enter the correct figures for the following costs which were not provided in part (a):

Direct materials used   £

Direct cost   £

Manufacturing cost   £

Cost of goods manufactured   £

Cost of goods sold   £

Task 9

You are told that the opening inventory of a single raw material in the stores is 1,200 units at £10.00 per unit. During the week 2,800 units at £8.00 are received and in the next week 3,200 units are issued.

(a) Identify the valuation method described in the statements below.

Statement	FIFO	LIFO	AVCO
The issue is costed at £27,520			
The closing inventory is valued at £8,000			
The closing inventory is valued at £6,400			

(b) Identify whether each of the statements below is true or false by putting a tick in the relevant column.

Statement	True	False
FIFO costs the issue at £23,200		
LIFO costs the issue at £26,400		
AVCO costs the issue at £27,520		

Task 10

A business has the following movements in a certain type of inventory into and out of its stores for the month of February:

Date	Receipts		Issues	
	Units	**Cost**	**Units**	**Cost**
February 5	100	£400		£
February 9	300	£1,260		£
February 13	600	£2,640		£
February 18			800	£
February 26	500	£2,150		£

Complete the table below for the issue costs and closing inventory values.

Method	Cost of Issue on 18 February	Value of Inventory at 28 February
FIFO	£	£
LIFO	£	£
AVCO	£	£

Task 11

(a) An employee is paid £9 per hour and is expected to produce 7 units an hour. Any production in excess of this is paid a bonus of £2.50 per unit.

Identify whether each of the statements below is true or false by putting a tick in the relevant column.

✔

Statement	True	False
If during a 40 hour week the employee produces 300 units a bonus of £50 will apply		
If during a 37 hour week the employee produces 250 units no bonus will apply		
If during a 39 hour week the employee produces 320 units a bonus of £67.50 will apply		

(b) A company pays a time-rate of £11.00 per hour for a 38 hour week. Any hours worked in excess of 38 are paid at an overtime rate of £16.50.

Calculate the relevant figures and insert them into the following table for the two employees shown.

Employee	Hours Worked	Basic Wage	Overtime	Gross Wage
S Leith	41	£	£	£
M Khan	39	£	£	£

Task 12

Piecework is a method of paying labour.

Identify whether each of the statements about piecework shown below is true or false by putting a tick in the relevant column.

✔

Statement	True	False
Employees' pay increases only if they work additional hours		
If an employee is paid £0.85 per unit they will earn £265 if they make 300 units		
If an employee paid by piecework earns £382.50 for producing 450 units, the rate is £0.85 per unit		
Employees who work faster are paid more than others who work slower for the same number of hours		

Task 13

A company uses a time-rate method with bonus to pay employees in its factory. The time-rate used is £9.50 per hour, and an employee is expected to produce 6 units per hour. For output in excess of this amount a bonus of £0.50 per unit is paid.

Calculate the pay of the three employees shown below by completing the table.

Employee	Hours Worked	Units Produced	Basic Wage £	Bonus £	Gross Wage £
M White	37	240			
P Truss	35	225			
N Collins	40	235			

Task 14

A company has produced the following partial cost and revenue information for a product in various months:

Sales revenue per unit: £10

Variable costs per unit:

    Materials   £5

    Labour   £2

A spreadsheet has been partly completed to record the total costs and revenue.

	A	B	C	D	E	F	G
1	Month	Variable Materials £	Variable Labour £		Total Costs £		Profit £
2	January	100,000	40,000	20,000	160,000	200,000	40,000
3	February	85,000		20,000			
4	March		38,000	20,000		190,000	
5	Total						

Required:

- Insert appropriate column headings into cells D1 and F1
  (select from: *Total Variable Costs £; Fixed Costs £; Total Costs £; Sales Revenue £*).

- Insert appropriate figures into the remaining cells in columns B, C, D, E, F.

- Insert appropriate formulas into the remaining cells in column G.

Task 15

Identify the following statements about spreadsheets as being true or false by putting a tick in the relevant column.

Statement	True	False
A cell is identified by its location letter followed by location number (eg C7)		
Every cell in a spreadsheet must always contain data – cells cannot be left blank		
Formulas can be used to automatically average the data in rows or columns		
A spreadsheet worksheet is a collection of spreadsheet workbooks		

Task 16

A company uses a spreadsheet to present budgeted and actual data and calculate profit and variances. The following spreadsheet has been partly completed.

	A	B	C	D	E
1		Budget £	Actual £	Variance £	A / F
2	Income	370,000	365,000		
3	Materials	121,500	120,600		
4	Labour	81,100	86,000		
5	Overheads	92,500	106,300		
6	Profit				

Required:

- Enter A or F into each cell in column E to denote adverse or favourable variances

- Enter appropriate formulas into the cells in column D to calculate variances, and into the remaining cells in row 6 to calculate profit.

Task 17

The following spreadsheet has been partly completed. Variances are considered significant if they exceed 3% of the budgeted amount.

Complete the spreadsheet as follows:

Complete column D with the amounts of the variances.

Show whether adverse (A) or Favourable (F) in column E.

Use 'S' to denote a significant variance or 'NS' to show a variance that is not significant in column F.

Complete column G with formulas to calculate each variance as a percentage of the relevant budget.

	A	B	C	D	E	F	G
1		Budget £	Actual £	Variance £	A / F	S/NS	Variance %
2	Income	153,500	146,000				
3	Materials	44,500	43,600				
4	Labour	41,100	43,000				
5	Overheads	49,500	51,300				

Practice
assessment 3

Task 1(a)

Identify the following statements as being true or false by putting a tick in the relevant column of the table below.

✔

Statement	True	False
LIFO is a method of valuing inventory issues and balances		
Budgets can be used to help monitor income and costs		
Budgets will always predict exactly what will happen in the future		
Variable costs per unit will remain the same as volumes change		

(b)

The table below lists some of the characteristics of financial accounting and management accounting systems.

Indicate which characteristics relate to each system by putting a tick in the relevant column of the table below.

✔

Characteristic	Financial Accounting	Management Accounting
One of its main outputs is a summarised historical financial statement that is produced annually		
One of its main purposes is useful information about costs within the organisation		
It can involve making comparisons between actual costs and budgeted costs		
Its output is controlled by legislation and accounting standards		

Task 2(a)

Roller Ltd is a manufacturer of garden equipment.

Classify the following costs into materials, labour and overheads by putting a tick in the relevant column of the table below.

✔

Cost	Materials	Labour	Overheads
Steel used to make garden forks			
Insurance of factory			
Wages of production workers			
Machinery maintenance contract			

(b)

Takeit Ltd is in business as a transport (haulage) company.

Classify the following costs by nature (direct or indirect) by putting a tick in the relevant column of the table below.

✔

Cost	Direct	Indirect
Lorry drivers' wages		
Cost of replacement tyres for lorries		
Wages of office administrator		
Motorway toll charges		

Task 3(a)

Roller Ltd manufactures garden equipment.

Classify the following costs by function (production, administration, selling and distribution or finance) by putting a tick in the relevant column of the table below.

✔

Cost	Production	Administration	Selling and Distribution	Finance
Purchases of wood for fork handles				
Costs of delivering garden equipment to retail outlets				
Loan interest				
Salaries of Administration Department staff				

(b)

Roller Ltd is a manufacturer of garden equipment.

Classify the following costs by their behaviour (fixed, variable, or semi-variable) by putting a tick in the relevant column of the table below.

✔

Cost	Fixed	Variable	Semi-Variable
Wood used to make fork handles			
Pay of Marketing Manager which includes a sales-based bonus			
Broadband costs which do not depend on internet usage			
Loan interest			

Task 4

Roller Limited is a manufacturer of garden equipment and uses a coding system for its elements of cost (materials labour or overhead expenses) and then further classifies each element by nature (direct or indirect cost) as below. So, for example, the code for direct materials is 50/100.

Element of Cost	Code	Nature of Cost	Code
Materials	50	Direct	100
		Indirect	200
Labour	60	Direct	100
		Indirect	200
Overhead Expenses	70	Direct	100
		Indirect	200

Code the following costs, extracted from invoices and payroll, using the table below.

Cost	Code
Wages of production worker	
Wages of delivery driver	
Steel to make garden spades	
Insurance for factory	
Repairs to factory roof	

Task 5

Zoom Ltd operates a garage business which comprises of second hand car sales and vehicle servicing. It uses an alpha-numeric coding structure based on one profit centre and three cost centres as outlined below. Each code has a sub-code so each transaction will be coded as */***

Profit/Cost Centre	Code	Sub-classification	Sub-code
Sales	W	Second Hand Car Sales	100
		Vehicle Servicing Sales	200
Second Hand Cars	X	Direct Cost	100
		Indirect Cost	200
Vehicle Servicing	Y	Direct Cost	100
		Indirect Cost	200
Administration	Z	Direct Cost	100
		Indirect Cost	200

Code the following revenue and cost transactions, which have been extracted from purchase invoices, sales invoices and payroll, using the table below.

Transaction	Code
Revenue from sale of Ford car to Mr Smith	
Cost of maintenance of electronic diagnostic equipment used for servicing vehicles	
Revenue from servicing vehicles during April	
Purchase cost of second hand cars at auction	
Cost of oil used to service vehicles	
Cost of wax used to polish cars ready for sale	

Task 6(a)

Identify the type of cost behaviour (fixed, variable or semi-variable) illustrated by each statement below by putting a tick in the relevant column of the table below.

✔

	Fixed	Variable	Semi-Variable
At 500 units, costs total £3,500, and at 1,500 units costs total £10,500			
At 500 units, costs total £6,500, and at 1,500 units costs total £13,500			
At 500 units, costs are £10 per unit, and at 1,000 units costs are £5 per unit			

(b)

Classify the following costs as either fixed or variable by putting a tick in the relevant column of the table below.

✔

Cost	Fixed	Variable
Interest on loan used to purchase factory		
Pay for production workers based on a fixed amount per unit produced		
Salaries of accounts office staff		
Wages of factory cleaning staff based on regular hours		

Task 7(a)

Identify the following statements as true or false by putting a tick in the relevant column of the table below.

✔

	True	False
Direct material costs normally behave as variable costs		
Indirect costs cannot be identified specifically with the product made		

(b)

Eureka Ltd makes a single product and for a production level of 20,000 units has the following cost details:

Materials 2,000 kilos at £18 per kilo

Labour 4,000 hours at £12 an hour

Fixed Overheads £60,000

Complete the table below to show the unit cost at the production level of 20,000 units.

	Unit Cost
Materials	£
Labour	£
Overheads	£
Total	£

Task 8(a)

Reorder the following costs into a manufacturing account format on the right side of the table below.

	£		£
Direct cost			
Purchases of raw materials	111,000		
Opening inventory of raw materials	23,000		
Closing inventory of finished goods	38,000		
Direct labour	176,000		
Cost of goods manufactured			
Cost of goods sold			
Manufacturing cost			
Direct materials used			
Opening inventory of work in progress	37,000		
Opening inventory of finished goods	55,000		
Manufacturing overheads	126,000		
Closing inventory of work in progress	49,000		
Closing inventory of raw materials	17,000		

(b)

Calculate the following amounts relating to part (a):

Direct materials used   £

Direct cost   £

Manufacturing cost   £

Cost of goods manufactured   £

Cost of goods sold   £

Task 9(a)

You are told that the opening inventory of a single raw material in the stores is 800 units at £12 per unit. During the period a receipt of 1,000 units at £11 per units is received, followed by an issue of 1,500 units.

Identify the valuation method described in the statements below.

Statement	FIFO	LIFO	AVCO
The closing inventory is valued at £3,600			
The issue of 1,500 units is costed at £17,300			
The closing inventory is valued at £3,300			

(b)

Identify whether the following statements are true or false by putting a tick in the relevant column of the table below.

	True	False
AVCO values issues at the weighted average cost of the inventory		
FIFO values issues at the most recent purchase price(s)		
LIFO values issues at the most recent purchase price(s)		
FIFO values inventory at the weighted average cost of the inventory		
LIFO values inventory at the most recent purchase price(s)		
FIFO values inventory at the most recent purchase price(s)		

Task 10

Nelson Ltd has the following movements in a certain type of inventory into and out of its stores for the month of February:

Date	Receipts		Issues	
	Units	**Cost**	**Units**	**Cost**
February 5	50	£400		£
February 9	150	£1,275		£
February 13	300	£2,550		£
February 18			400	£
February 26	250	£2,250		£

Complete the table below for the issue and closing inventory values.

Method	Value of Issue on 18 February	Inventory at 28 February
FIFO	£	£
LIFO	£	£
AVCO	£	£

Task 11(a)

Identify one feature for each labour payment method by putting a tick in the relevant column of the table below.

✔

Payment Method	Time-rate	Piecework	Time-rate plus bonus
All employees earn at least a certain amount, but efficient employees are rewarded with additional amounts			
Efficient employees will earn the same amount as inefficient employees			
An employee's pay would double if his output doubled			

(b)

Nelson Ltd pays a time-rate of £9 per hour to its direct labour for a standard 38 hour week. Any of the labour force working in excess of 38 hours is paid an overtime rate of £13.50 per hour.

Calculate the gross wage for the week for the two workers in the table below.

Worker	Hours Worked	Basic Wage	Overtime	Gross Wage
M Singh	38	£	£	£
S Spencer	43	£	£	£

Task 12

Nelson Ltd uses a piecework method to pay labour in one of its factories. The rate used is £3.09 per unit produced.

Calculate the gross wage for the week for the two workers in the table below.

Worker	Units Produced in Week	Gross Wage
G Purcell	89	£
M Katz	103	£

Task 13

Nelson Ltd uses a time-rate method with bonus to pay its direct labour in one of its factories. The time-rate used is £8.50 per hour and a worker is expected to produce 4 units an hour. Anything over this and the worker is paid a bonus of £1.50 per unit.

Calculate the gross wage for the week including bonus for the three workers in the table below.

Worker	Hours Worked	Units Produced	Basic Wage	Bonus	Gross Wage
J Jarvis	40	150	£	£	£
S Poole	40	185	£	£	£
D Kerr	40	173	£	£	£

Task 14

A company has produced the following partial cost and revenue information for a product in various months:

Sales revenue per unit:　　　　£30

Variable costs per unit:

　　Materials　　　　　　　£12

　　Labour　　　　　　　　£5

A spreadsheet has been partly completed to record the total costs and revenue.

	A	B	C	D	E	F	G
1	Month	Variable Materials £	Variable Labour £	Fixed Costs £	Total Costs £		
2	Jan	72,000	30,000	40,000	142,000	180,000	38,000
3	Feb	144,000					
4	March		45,000	40,000			
5	Total						

Required:

- Insert appropriate column headings into cells F1 and G1
  (select from: Total Variable Costs £; Total Fixed Costs £; Total Costs £; Sales Revenue £; Profit £).

- Insert appropriate figures into the remaining cells in rows 3 and 4.

- Insert appropriate formulas into the cells in row 5.

Task 15

Identify the following statements about spreadsheets as being true or false by putting a tick in the relevant column.

Statement	True	False
The contents of a spreadsheet cell could be manually inputted data or the results of a formula		
Spreadsheet cells can contain words and / or numbers		
Formulas can be used to automatically calculate percentages		
Columns or rows can be sorted into ascending or descending order		

Task 16

A company uses a spreadsheet to present budgeted and actual data and calculate profit and variances. The following spreadsheet has been partly completed.

	A	B	C	D	E
1		Budget £	Actual £	Variance £	A / F
2	Income	140,000	136,000		
3	Materials	24,500	23,600		
4	Labour	41,100	39,000		
5	Overheads	52,500	55,300		
6	Profit				

Required:

- Enter A or F into each cell in column E to denote adverse or favourable variances.

- Enter profit figures into cells B6 and C6.

- Enter appropriate formulas into the cells in column D to calculate variances.

Task 17

The following spreadsheet has been partly completed. Variances are considered significant if they exceed 10% of the budgeted amount.

(a) Complete the spreadsheet as follows:

Complete column D with the amounts of the variances.

Show whether adverse (A) or Favourable (F) in column E.

Use 'S' to denote a significant variance or 'NS' to show a variance that is not significant in column F.

	A	B	C	D	E	F
1		Budget £	Actual £	Variance £	A / F	S/NS
2	Income	355,500	376,000			
3	Materials	152,500	171,600			
4	Labour	91,100	78,000			
5	Overheads	70,500	69,300			

(b) If the spreadsheet was to be sorted to show the smallest variance first, which of the following functions would need to be used in conjunction with column D?

- Average
- Ascending
- Descending
- Autosum

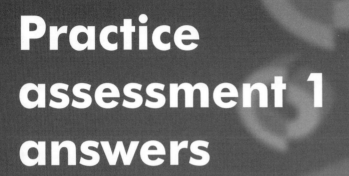

Practice assessment 1 answers

Task 1(a)

Statement	True	False
LIFO is a method of paying labour		✔
Standard costs may be used to help build budgets	✔	
Variances can measure the difference between budgeted and actual income and costs	✔	
Fixed costs will never change in the future whatever happens		✔

(b)

Characteristic	Financial Accounting	Management Accounting
It is concerned with recording historic costs and revenues	✔	
One of its main purposes is to provide information for annual financial statements	✔	
It is accurate, with no use of estimates	✔	
It looks forward to show what is likely to happen in the future		✔

Task 2(a)

Cost	Materials	Labour	Overheads
Meat used in burgers	✔		
Electricity used in factory			✔
Boxes to pack burgers	✔		
Expenses of the sales manager			✔

(b)

Cost	Direct	Indirect
Fuel for taxis	✔	
Cost of servicing taxis		✔
Wages of taxi drivers	✔	
Wages of reception staff		✔

Task 3(a)

Cost	Production	Administration	Selling and Distribution
Purchases of components for mobile telephones	✔		
Commission paid to sales staff			✔
Rent of offices		✔	
Wages of staff who assemble telephones	✔		

(b)

Cost	Fixed	Variable	Semi-Variable
Labour costs paid on a time basis	✔		
Maintenance of website	✔		
Power costs which include a standing charge			✔
Packing materials for completed instruments		✔	

Task 4

Cost	Code
Wages of taxi driver	60/100
Vehicle insurance for taxis	70/200
Wages of reception staff	60/200
Fuel for taxis	50/100
Office rent	70/200

Task 5

Transaction	Code
Factory lighting	B/200
Repairs to warehouse	D/200
Meat for making burgers	B/100
Sales to 'Kings Restaurant'	A/100
Commission to sales staff	D/200
Stationery for Administration	C/200

Task 6(a)

	True	False
Variable costs change in proportion to changes in activity level	✔	
Fixed costs remain unchanged when activity levels change	✔	
Semi-variable costs change in proportion to changes in activity level		✔

(b)

Cost	Fixed	Variable
Factory insurance	✔	
Bonus for production staff paid per item produced		✔
Salaries of administration staff	✔	
Repairs to a factory used for production	✔	

Task 7(a)

	True	False
Direct material costs cannot be identified with the goods being made or the service being produced		✔
Indirect costs never change when the level of activity alters		✔

(b)

Element	Unit Cost
Materials	£3.00
Labour	£2.75
Overheads	£4.00
Total	£9.75

Task 8(a)

	£		£
Closing inventory of raw materials	10,000	Opening inventory of raw materials	9,000
Direct labour	86,000	Purchases of raw materials	48,000
Opening inventory of raw materials	9,000	Closing inventory of raw materials	10,000
Closing inventory of finished goods	25,000	Direct materials used	
Direct cost		Direct labour	86,000
Cost of goods manufactured		Direct cost	
Cost of sales		Manufacturing overheads	64,000
Manufacturing cost		Manufacturing cost	
Purchases of raw materials	48,000	Opening inventory of work in progress	9,000
Opening inventory of work in progress	9,000	Closing inventory of work in progress	11,000
Opening inventory of finished goods	30,000	Cost of goods manufactured	
Manufacturing overheads	64,000	Opening inventory of finished goods	30,000
Direct materials used		Closing inventory of finished goods	25,000
Closing inventory of work in progress	11,000	Cost of sales	

(b)

Direct materials used	£47,000
Direct cost	£133,000
Manufacturing cost	£197,000
Cost of goods manufactured	£195,000
Cost of sales	£200,000

Task 9(a)

Characteristic	FIFO	LIFO	AVCO
Inventory is valued at the most recent purchase cost	✔		
Issues are valued at the average of the cost of purchases			✔
Issues are valued at the oldest relevant purchase cost	✔		

9(b)

	True	False
AVCO costs issues of inventory at the most recent purchase price		✔
FIFO costs issues of inventory at the oldest relevant purchase price	✔	
LIFO costs issues of inventory at the oldest relevant purchase price		✔
FIFO values closing inventory at the most recent purchase price	✔	
LIFO values closing inventory at the most recent purchase price		✔
AVCO values closing inventory at the most recent purchase price		✔

Task 10

Method	Value of Issue on 18 August	Inventory at 31 August
FIFO	£3,695	£2,505
LIFO	£3,760	£2,440
AVCO	£3,722	£2,478

Task 11(a)

Payment Method	Time-rate	Piecework	Time-rate plus bonus
Labour is paid based entirely on attendance at the workplace	✔		
Labour is paid a basic rate plus an extra amount if an agreed level of production is exceeded			✔
Labour is paid entirely according to each individual's output		✔	

(b)

Worker	Hours Worked	Basic Wage	Overtime	Gross Wage
A Smith	37	£296.00	£0.00	£296.00
S Collins	41	£296.00	£64.00	£360.00

Task 12

Worker	Units Produced in Week	Gross Wage
G Powell	109	£235.44
S Singh	123	£265.68

Task 13

Worker	Hours Worked	Units Produced	Basic Wage	Bonus	Gross Wage
A Weaton	40	250	£400.00	£0.00	£400.00
J Davis	40	295	£400.00	£7.50	£407.50
M Laston	40	280	£400.00	£0.00	£400.00

Task 14

	A	B	C	D	E	F	G
1	Month	Variable Materials £	Variable Labour £	Fixed Costs £	Total Costs £	Sales Revenue £	Profit £
2	January	70,000	30,000	40,000	140,000	200,000	60,000
3	February	140,000	60,000	40,000	240,000	400,000	160,000
4	March	105,000	45,000	40,000	190,000	300,000	110,000
5	Total	=B2+B3+B4	=C2+C3+C4	=D2+D3+D4	=E2+E3+E4	=F2+F3+F4	=G2+G3+G4

Task 15

Statement	True	False
A cell is identified by its location number followed by location letter (eg 6C)		✔
Every cell in a spreadsheet must always contain a formula		✔
Formulas can be used to automatically total rows or columns	✔	
A spreadsheet workbook is a collection of spreadsheet worksheets	✔	

Task 16

	A	B	C	D	E
1		Budget £	Actual £	Variance £	A / F
2	Income	290,000	296,000	=C2-B2	F
3	Materials	144,500	150,600	=C3-B3	A
4	Labour	51,100	49,000	=B4-C4	F
5	Overheads	72,500	76,300	=C5-B5	A
6	Profit	=B2-B3-B4-B5	=C2-C3-C4-C5	=B6-C6	A

Note: other valid formulas could be used

Task 17(a)

	A	B	C	D	E	F
1		Budget £	Actual £	Variance £	A / F	S/NS
2	Income	173,500	176,000	2,500	F	NS
3	Materials	62,500	71,600	9,100	A	S
4	Labour	31,100	38,000	6,900	A	S
5	Overheads	60,500	59,300	1,200	F	NS

(b) • Descending

Practice
assessment 2
answers

Task 1(a)

	True	False
AVCO is a method of valuing inventory issues and balances	✔	
One method of labour payment is to pay a basic hourly rate for normal working hours, and an enhanced rate for overtime hours	✔	
Variances can only be used to measure the difference between budgeted and actual costs (not income)		✔
A fixed cost per unit will always remain unchanged as output volumes change		✔

(b)

Characteristic	Financial Accounting	Management Accounting
The system is subject to many external regulations	✔	
The accounts must be produced in a format that is imposed on the organisation	✔	
The system is governed primarily by its usefulness to its internal users		✔
The information produced can be in any format that the organisation wishes to use		✔

Task 2(a)

Cost	Material	Labour	Overhead
Factory rent			✔
Steel for manufacturing wheel spokes	✔		
Pay of staff who assemble wheels		✔	
Factory lighting			✔

(b)

Cost	Direct	Indirect
Cost of paying factory supervisor		✔
Cost of paying factory cleaner		✔
Cost of repairs to factory electrical system		✔
Cost of factory insurance		✔

Task 3(a)

Cost	Production	Administration	Selling and Distribution	Finance
Cost of paying factory supervisor	✔			
Cost of servicing of delivery vehicles			✔	
Cost of advertisements			✔	
Cost of arrangement fee for bank overdraft				✔

(b)

Cost	Fixed	Variable	Semi-Variable
Cost of paying wheel assemblers on a piecework basis		✔	
Cost of renting factory premises	✔		
Cost of advertisements	✔		
Cost of paying a production supervisor on a basic pay plus a production-based bonus			✔

Task 4

Transaction	Code
Wages of administration assistant	700/040
Cost of producing sales catalogue	800/060
Sales of men's swimming trunks	500/085
Purchase of material to make clothing	600/010
Wages of production supervisor	600/020
Cost of renting photocopier for administration department	700/040

Task 5

Transaction	Code
Revenue from project in Saudi Arabia	PR200
Cost of material used for project in Saudi Arabia	PC030
Cost of hiring local labour for project in Saudi Arabia	PC040
Investment in project in Saudi Arabia	IP200
Revenue from UK project	PR100
Cost of renting project offices	PC050

Task 6(a)

Statement	Fixed	Variable	Semi-Variable
Costs are £4,000 in total for 1,000 units, and £6,000 in total for 1,500 units		✔	
Costs of £20,000 in total for 2,000 units are made up of £10,000 plus £5 per unit			✔
Costs are £5 per unit at 20,000 units and £10 per unit at 10,000 units	✔		

(b)

Cost	Fixed	Variable
Cost of factory insurance	✔	
Cost of interest on a bank loan	✔	
Cost of raw materials used to manufacture products		✔

Task 7(a)

Cost	Yes	No
Cost of factory insurance		✔
Cost of interest on a bank loan		✔
Cost of raw materials used to manufacture products	✔	

(b)

Element	Unit Product Cost
Direct materials	£2
Direct labour	£1
Direct cost	£3
Overheads	£5
Total cost	£8

Task 8(a)

	£		£
Direct cost		Opening inventory of raw materials	13,000
Purchases of raw materials	123,000	Purchases of raw materials	123,000
Opening inventory of raw materials	13,000	Closing inventory of raw materials	27,000
Closing inventory of finished goods	33,000	Direct materials used	
Direct labour	156,000	Direct labour	156,000
Cost of goods manufactured		Direct cost	
Cost of goods sold		Manufacturing overheads	146,000
Manufacturing cost		Manufacturing cost	
Direct materials used		Opening inventory of work in progress	27,000
Opening inventory of work in progress	27,000	Closing inventory of work in progress	39,000
Opening inventory of finished goods	35,000	Cost of goods manufactured	
Manufacturing overheads	146,000	Opening inventory of finished goods	35,000
Closing inventory of work in progress	39,000	Closing inventory of finished goods	33,000
Closing inventory of raw materials	27,000	Cost of goods sold	

(b)

Direct materials used	£109,000
Direct cost	£265,000
Manufacturing cost	£411,000
Cost of goods manufactured	£399,000
Cost of goods sold	£401,000

Task 9

(a)

Statement	FIFO	LIFO	AVCO
The issue is costed at £27,520			✔
The closing inventory is valued at £8,000		✔	
The closing inventory is valued at £6,400	✔		

(b)

Statement	True	False
FIFO costs the issue at £23,200		✔
LIFO costs the issue at £26,400	✔	
AVCO costs the issue at £27,520	✔	

Task 10

Method	Cost of Issue on 18 February	Value of Inventory at 28 February
FIFO	£3,420	£3,030
LIFO	£3,480	£2,970
AVCO	£3,440	£3,010

Task 11(a)

Statement	True	False
If during a 40 hour week the employee produces 300 units a bonus of £50 will apply	✔	
If during a 37 hour week the employee produces 250 units no bonus will apply	✔	
If during a 39 hour week the employee produces 320 units a bonus of £67.50 will apply		✔

(b)

Employee	Hours Worked	Basic Wage	Overtime	Gross Wage
S Leith	41	£418.00	£49.50	£467.50
M Khan	39	£418.00	£16.50	£434.50

Task 12

Statement	True	False
Employees' pay increases only if they work additional hours		✔
If an employee is paid £0.85 per unit they will earn £265 if they make 300 units		✔
If an employee paid by piecework earns £382.50 for producing 450 units, the rate is £0.85 per unit	✔	
Employees who work faster are paid more than others who work slower for the same number of hours	✔	

Task 13

Employee	Hours Worked	Units Produced	Basic Wage £	Bonus £	Gross Wage £
M White	37	240	351.50	9.00	360.50
P Truss	35	225	332.50	7.50	340.00
N Collins	40	235	380.00	0.00	380.00

Task 14

	A	B	C	D	E	F	G
1	Month	Variable Materials £	Variable Labour £	Fixed Costs £	Total Costs £	Sales Revenue £	Profit £
2	January	100,000	40,000	20,000	160,000	200,000	40,000
3	February	85,000	34,000	20,000	139,000	170,000	=F3-E3
4	March	95,000	38,000	20,000	153,000	190,000	=F4-E4
5	Total	280,000	112,000	60,000	452,000	560,000	=F5-E5

Note: other valid formulas could also be used.

Task 15

Statement	True	False
A cell is identified by its location letter followed by location number (eg C7)	✔	
Every cell in a spreadsheet must always contain data – cells cannot be left blank		✔
Formulas can be used to automatically average the data in rows or columns	✔	
A spreadsheet worksheet is a collection of spreadsheet workbooks		✔

Task 16

	A	B	C	D	E
1		Budget £	Actual £	Variance £	A / F
2	Income	370,000	365,000	=B2-C2	A
3	Materials	121,500	120,600	=B3-C3	F
4	Labour	81,100	86,000	=C4-B4	A
5	Overheads	92,500	106,300	=C5-B5	A
6	Profit	=B2-B3-B4-B5	=C2-C3-C4-C5	=B6-C6	A

Note: other valid formulas could also be used.

Task 17

	A	B	C	D	E	F	G
1		Budget £	Actual £	Variance £	A / F	S/NS	Variance %
2	Income	153,500	146,000	7,500	A	S	=D2/B2%
3	Materials	44,500	43,600	900	F	NS	=D3/B3%
4	Labour	41,100	43,000	1,900	A	S	=D4/B4%
5	Overheads	49,500	51,300	1,800	A	S	=D5/B5%

Note: other valid formulas could also be used.

Practice
assessment 3
answers

Task 1(a)

Statement	True	False
LIFO is a method of valuing inventory issues and balances	✔	
Budgets can be used to help monitor income and costs	✔	
Budgets will always predict exactly what will happen in the future		✔
Variable costs per unit will remain the same as volumes change	✔	

(b)

Characteristic	Financial Accounting	Management Accounting
One of its main outputs is a summarised historical financial statement that is produced annually	✔	
One of its main purposes is useful information about costs within the organisation		✔
It can involve making comparisons between actual costs and budgeted costs		✔
Its output is controlled by legislation and accounting standards	✔	

Task 2(a)

Cost	Materials	Labour	Overheads
Steel used to make garden forks	✔		
Insurance of factory			✔
Wages of production workers		✔	
Machinery maintenance contract			✔

(b)

Cost	Direct	Indirect
Lorry drivers' wages	✔	
Cost of replacement tyres for lorries		✔
Wages of office administrator		✔
Motorway toll charges	✔	

Task 3(a)

Cost	Production	Administration	Selling and Distribution	Finance
Purchases of wood for fork handles	✔			
Costs of delivering garden equipment to retail outlets			✔	
Loan interest				✔
Salaries of Administration Department staff		✔		

(b)

Cost	Fixed	Variable	Semi-Variable
Wood used to make fork handles		✔	
Pay of Marketing Manager which includes a sales-based bonus			✔
Broadband costs which do not depend on internet usage	✔		
Loan interest	✔		

Task 4

Cost	Code
Wages of production worker	60/100
Wages of delivery driver	60/200
Steel to make garden spades	50/100
Insurance for factory	70/200
Repairs to factory roof	70/200

Task 5

Transaction	Code
Revenue from sale of Ford car to Mr Smith	W/100
Cost of maintenance of electronic diagnostic equipment used for servicing vehicles	Y/200
Revenue from servicing vehicles during April	W/200
Purchase cost of second hand cars at auction	X/100
Cost of oil used to service vehicles	Y/100
Cost of wax used to polish cars ready for sale	X/200

Task 6(a)

	Fixed	Variable	Semi-Variable
At 500 units, costs total £3,500, and at 1,500 units costs total £10,500		✔	
At 500 units, costs total £6,500, and at 1,500 units costs total £13,500			✔
At 500 units, costs are £10 per unit, and at 1,000 units costs are £5 per unit	✔		

(b)

Cost	Fixed	Variable
Interest on loan used to purchase factory	✔	
Pay for production workers based on a fixed amount per unit produced		✔
Salaries of accounts office staff	✔	
Wages of factory cleaning staff based on regular hours	✔	

Task 7(a)

	True	False
Direct material costs normally behave as variable costs	✔	
Indirect costs cannot be identified specifically with the product made	✔	

(b)

	Unit Cost
Materials	£1.80
Labour	£2.40
Overheads	£3.00
Total	£7.20

Task 8(a)

	£
Opening inventory of raw materials	23,000
Purchases of raw materials	111,000
Closing inventory of raw materials	17,000
Direct materials used	
Direct labour	176,000
Direct cost	
Manufacturing overheads	126,000
Manufacturing cost	
Opening inventory of work in progress	37,000
Closing inventory of work in progress	49,000
Cost of goods manufactured	
Opening inventory of finished goods	55,000
Closing inventory of finished goods	38,000
Cost of goods sold	

(b)

Direct material used	£117,000
Direct cost	£293,000
Manufacturing cost	£419,000
Cost of goods manufactured	£407,000
Cost of goods sold	£424,000

Task 9(a)

Statement	FIFO	LIFO	AVCO
The closing inventory is valued at £3,600		✔	
The issue of 1,500 units is costed at £17,300	✔		
The closing inventory is valued at £3,300	✔		

9(b)

	True	False
AVCO values issues at the weighted average cost of the inventory	✔	
FIFO values issues at the most recent purchase price(s)		✔
LIFO values issues at the most recent purchase price(s)	✔	
FIFO values inventory at the weighted average cost of the inventory		✔
LIFO values inventory at the most recent purchase price(s)		✔
FIFO values inventory at the most recent purchase price(s)	✔	

Task 10

Method	Value of Issue on 18 February	Inventory at 28 February
FIFO	£3,375	£3,100
LIFO	£3,400	£3,075
AVCO	£3,380	£3,095

Task 11(a)

Payment Method	Time-rate	Piecework	Time-rate plus bonus
All employees earn at least a certain amount, but efficient employees are rewarded with additional amounts			✔
Efficient employees will earn the same amount as inefficient employees	✔		
An employee's pay would double if his output doubled		✔	

(b)

Worker	Hours Worked	Basic Wage	Overtime	Gross Wage
M Singh	38	£342.00	£0.00	£342.00
S Spencer	43	£342.00	£67.50	£409.50

Task 12

Worker	Units Produced in Week	Gross Wage
G Purcell	89	£275.01
M Katz	103	£318.27

Task 13

Worker	Hours Worked	Units Produced	Basic Wage	Bonus	Gross Wage
J Jarvis	40	150	£340.00	£0.00	£340.00
S Poole	40	185	£340.00	£37.50	£377.50
D Kerr	40	173	£340.00	£19.50	£359.50

Task 14

	A	B	C	D	E	F	G
1	Month	Variable Materials £	Variable Labour £	Fixed Costs £		Sales Revenue £	Profit £
2	Jan	72,000	30,000	40,000	142,000	180,000	38,000
3	Feb	144,000	60,000	40,000	244,000	360,000	116,000
4	March	108,000	45,000	40,000	193,000	270,000	77,000
5	Total	=SUM(B2:B4)	=SUM(C2:C4)	=SUM(D2:D4)	=SUM(E2:E4)	=SUM(F2:F4)	=SUM(G2:G4)

Task 15

Statement	True	False
The contents of a spreadsheet cell could be manually inputted data or the results of a formula	✔	
Spreadsheet cells can contain words and / or numbers	✔	
Formulas can be used to automatically calculate percentages	✔	
Columns or rows can be sorted into ascending or descending order	✔	

Task 16

	A	B	C	D	E
1		Budget £	Actual £	Variance £	A / F
2	Income	140,000	136,000	=B2-C2	A
3	Materials	24,500	23,600	=B3-C3	F
4	Labour	41,100	39,000	=B4-C4	F
5	Overheads	52,500	55,300	=C5-B5	A
6	Profit	21,900	18,100	=B6-C6	A

Task 17(a)

	A	B	C	D	E	F
1		Budget £	Actual £	Variance £	A / F	S/NS
2	Income	355,500	376,000	20,500	F	NS
3	Materials	152,500	171,600	19,100	A	S
4	Labour	91,100	78,000	13,100	F	S
5	Overheads	70,500	69,300	1,200	F	NS

(b) • Ascending